William Shakespeare
King Lear

Retold by
Marcia Williams

WALKER
BOOKS

Contents

In which Lear divides his kingdom.

In ancient Britain, the elderly King Lear was feeling tired. The burdens of state had worn him down and in his old age he just wanted to enjoy being king. So Lear decided to divide his kingdom among his three daughters, keeping only the crown for himself. Excited by the prospect of giving up his lands and power and being able to relax, he summoned his daughters to his palace

along with all his knights and nobles. There,
on a fond father's whim, he declared that
he would give the largest territory to the
daughter who professed to love him best.

The gathered lords and nobles frowned at
this division of the kingdom, particularly the
Earl of Kent, Lear's loyal friend. However,
the old king was in no doubt that his

favourite and youngest daughter, Cordelia, would profess the deepest love. So he sat on his throne, happily waiting to bask in his daughters' declarations of adoration.

His eldest daughter, greedy Goneril of Albany, was the first to respond. She cared not one jot for her father, but she cared for power and wealth, so she pretended to love her father very much indeed. "Sir," she cried on bended knee, "I do love you more than words can wield the matter; dearer than

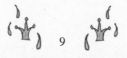

eyesight, space, and liberty." When Goneril
was finished, King Lear clapped his old
hands in delight and gave her one third of
his kingdom.

Then came Lear's second daughter, Regan
of Cornwall, with white, wafer-thin lips.
Regan's love was as shallow as her greed
was deep, but she swore she loved her father
even more than Goneril did. "I am made of
that self mettle as my sister," she said. "Only
she comes too short." For her false words,

Lear gave Regan a portion of his kingdom to match Goneril's.

Then Lear turned to his youngest, Cordelia. "Now, our joy," he said proudly. "What can you say to draw a third more opulent than your sisters? Speak."

"Nothing, my lord," replied Cordelia.

"Nothing?" exclaimed the king, hardly able to believe his ears.

"Nothing," said Cordelia.

"Nothing will come of nothing. Speak again," shouted the king.

Poor Cordelia was unable to put her thoughts into words – she loved her father so much and so truly. She had been sickened by her sisters' false words, and she could not bring herself to compete with their falsehood. All her young life, Cordelia had shown her father both love and respect. Surely she had nothing to prove?

"I love Your Majesty according to my bond," said Cordelia. "No more nor less."

"So young, and so untender?" cried her father.

"So young, my lord, and true," replied Cordelia.

At this, Lear flew into a rage. He felt that Cordelia had made a fool of him in front of his whole court. He disowned Cordelia and divided the best lands that he had saved for her between Goneril and Regan.

"Check this hideous rashness," cried the Earl of Kent. Kent  could not believe that Lear had trusted his two stone-hearted daughters and not understood his youngest daughter's true and loving heart. But Lear was in no mood to listen to anyone. He banished Kent on the spot. "Away! If thy banish'd trunk be found in our dominions, the

moment is thy death!" the king roared.

Kent was not the only noble to admire and understand Cordelia's honesty. Her suitor, the King of France, was moved by her brave conduct. Far from deserting her now that she was without an inheritance, he asked her to marry him.

"Fairest Cordelia, that art most rich, being poor. Thee and thy virtues here I seize upon," he said.

"Thou hast her, France," snarled Lear, "let her be thine, for we have no such daughter."

So Cordelia prepared to sail for France, reluctantly leaving her father in the care of her cunning sisters.

In which Goneril and Regan betray their father.

The banished Kent could see troubled times ahead for Lear and could not bring himself to leave his old friend. He disguised himself as a commoner and took a job as Lear's servant, hoping to protect him from his scheming daughters.

Lear had no palace of his own now, so
he took one hundred knights, his fool and
his new servant to stay with Goneril, in
a castle that just hours before had been
his. Goneril and her husband, the Duke of

Albany, made no pretence of welcoming the
old king. Goneril was no longer the daughter
full of loving promises, for she already had
everything her father had to give – she had
even taken his crown. As the days went by,
Goneril treated the king without any love

or respect. Soon even Goneril's servants refused to do the king's bidding.

"How now, daughter?" said Lear. "Methinks you are too much of late i' th' frown."

"Here do you keep a hundred knights and squires," she snapped back at him. "Men so disordered, so debauched and bold that this our court, infected with their manners, shows like a riotous inn."

This was quite untrue, for the king's knights and squires were noble men who had been with him for many years. King Lear was stung by his daughter's ingratitude, and tears came to his eyes.

"How sharper than a serpent's tooth it is to have a thankless child!" he cried. "I have another daughter, who, I am sure, is kind and comfortable."

Bewildered by Goneril's harshness, Lear decided to visit Regan, who he felt sure would be kinder. He sent his new servant ahead to the Earl of Gloucester's palace where Regan and her husband, the Duke of Cornwall, were staying. Then he, his knights and his loyal fool followed, galloping wildly through the night.

They arrived at Gloucester's palace as
dawn broke – but there was no welcome
for them there. All that greeted them was
Lear's servant in the stocks. Lear was
outraged that a servant of his had been
treated with such disrespect. "They durst
not do't; They could not, would not do't,"
muttered the king, fearing that he might be
going mad.

He sent for Regan to come and explain
herself. She came out with Goneril by her
side. Lear realized that Goneril had ridden
ahead and that his two daughters had
joined forces against him. They told Lear
he must give up his knights and live as a
pauper.

"What need you five-and-twenty, ten, or
five?" snapped Goneril.

"What need one?" said Regan through her thin white lips.

"I gave you all!" the king cried out. He had no other daughter left to turn to. How bitterly he regretted casting off Cordelia.

King Lear rushed out onto the heath in a pitiless storm, his mind twisting in pain and sorrow. The lashing rain was nothing compared with the lashing tongues of his daughters. Lear's fool, and

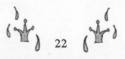

his faithful companion, Kent, ran after him.

"O Fool! I shall go mad!" Lear shouted
through the wind. "Blow, winds, and crack
your cheeks! Rage! Blow!"

The Earl of Gloucester, powerless against

Goneril and Regan, sadly watched Lear stumble across the heath. He too had suffered at the hands of his children. His youngest son, Edmund, had told him that Edgar, his favourite son, planned to murder him. This was a lie, but Gloucester had believed it and had driven Edgar away. He did not know that Edgar was living nearby in a hovel on the heath, disguised as a mad beggar. It was into this very hovel that Kent and the fool dragged King Lear for shelter.

"He that has a little tiny wit,
    With hey, ho, the wind and the rain,
    Must make content with his fortunes fit,
    Though the rain it raineth every day,"
sang the fool, brushing the rain off the king.

Edgar cowered in the shadows, naked but

for an old rag around his waist, delirious with cold and misery. "Pillicock sat on Pillicock Hill," Edgar cried. "Halloo, halloo, loo, loo!"

"This cold night will turn us all to fools and madmen," shivered the fool.

"Tom's a-cold," moaned Edgar.

The old king looked at this bundle of jabbering rags with pity. "Didst thou give all to thy two daughters?" he asked. "And art thou come to this?"

The wind and the rain continued to howl outside while King Lear and his motley companions tried to shut their eyes to the night and the biting cold.

In which events take a gruesome turn.

Back at the palace, Gloucester overheard Regan and Goneril plotting to kill King Lear. Bravely he rushed out into the night to warn Kent.

"Come hither, friend: where is the king, my master?" he said.

"Here, sir; but trouble him not. His wits are gone," Kent replied.

"I have o'erheard a plot of death upon him.

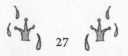

There is a litter ready; lay him in it and drive towards Dover," said brave Gloucester. So Kent and the fool carried King Lear towards the coast.

On his return to the castle, Gloucester discovered that he had been seen helping the old king. On the orders of Goneril and Regan, he was dragged across the great hall of the castle and bound fast to a chair.

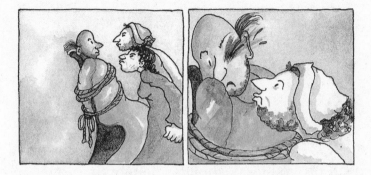

"I shall see the winged vengeance overtake such children," he cried bravely.

"See't shalt thou never," cried Cornwall, and brutally tore out one of his eyes.

A shocked servant tried to intervene. He was swiftly killed, but not before he had

wounded Cornwall. Oblivious to his wound and urged on by Regan, Cornwall took out Gloucester's

other eye. "Out, vile jelly!" he cried.

When Regan heard that Cornwall's wound had proved fatal, she was delighted. Now her husband was dead, she was free to marry Gloucester's scheming son, Edmund, whom she loved. Unfortunately Goneril

loved him too, and was consumed with jealousy. She wrote to Edmund suggesting he kill her husband, Albany, leaving her free to marry him.

In which Lear and Cordelia are reunited.

The sisters had to put their battle for Edmund to one side: news came that Cordelia, having heard of her father's plight, had raised a French army and

landed at Dover. The two sisters marshalled
their troops and set off to fight Cordelia.

Kent had also heard that Cordelia had
landed. He took Lear to look for her, hoping
to reunite father and daughter. Blind
Gloucester was on his way to Dover too,
with his son Edgar, who had found him lost
on the heath. Outside the port, Gloucester,

now eyeless, met Lear, mad with misery and fatigue. The king was almost naked and on his head he wore a lopsided crown made of flowers and herbs. "I am the king himself," he said. But none would have known it.

As the war drums rolled, Cordelia's servants came searching for the king. "O! Here he is; lay hand upon him," ordered the captain.

Poor Lear was more confused than ever

when he was carried to the French camp.

The surgeons would not let him see Cordelia until he had rested, as they feared that the shock of seeing her again might kill him.

When at last Lear woke and found Cordelia kneeling beside him, he could not believe his sad old eyes. "Do not laugh at me; for, as I am a man, I think this lady to be my child Cordelia," he said to Kent and the doctor.

"And so I am, I am," wept Cordelia, hardly able to bear the sight of what her cruel sisters had done to her father.

As Lear drifted in and out of sleep, Cordelia reluctantly left him, for the drums of war were still beating. King Lear slept through the long and hard-fought battle. When he awoke, Cordelia and the French had been defeated. Cordelia could have escaped, but she chose to stay with her father. Lear rejoiced, for the idea of imprisonment with Cordelia was heaven compared with liberty with Goneril and

Regan. He refused to try and bargain with them for his freedom. "No, no, no, no!" he cried to Cordelia. "Come, let's away to prison. We two alone will sing like birds i' the cage."

As Lear and Cordelia were led away, Edmund called the captain to him. He gave orders that they both should be killed.

In which the story is ended.

Shortly after the captain left to carry out this heartless deed, Albany arrived with Goneril and Regan. He had discovered Goneril and Edmund's plan to kill him! "Edmund, I arrest thee on capital treason, and this gilded serpent," he snarled, pointing to his wife.

But before the guards could lay hold of Edmund, an armoured man stepped from the crowd and challenged Edmund to a duel.

"Draw thy sword," cried the stranger.

Edmund accepted the challenge and the
duel began. Goneril and Regan watched
in horror as Edmund began to lose to his
unknown opponent. After the stranger

had delivered a mortal blow to Edmund, he removed his helmet and revealed himself. "My name is Edgar, and thy father's son," he said.

"The wheel is come full circle," sighed Edmund.

As Edmund lay dying, Edgar told him how he had been reunited with their father, Gloucester, just before his death.

A servant brought news that Goneril had poisoned Regan and then, realizing

Edmund would
not live, had killed
herself too. Edmund
was conscience-
stricken at last, for
he had promised to
marry both sisters. With his final breath he
told Edgar to send a reprieve for Lear and
Cordelia. "Nay, send in time," he cried.

"Run, run! O run!" cried out Albany,
appalled at the thought of more bloodshed.

It was too late. Lear's dearest Cordelia had been hanged. Albany and Edgar watched in horror as the old king stumbled towards them carrying her body in his arms.

"Howl, howl, howl, howl!" he wept. "O! You are men of stones: had I your tongues and eyes, I'd use them so that heaven's vaults should crack. She's gone forever."

Beside himself with grief, Lear fell into a faint. He had lost everything – what he had not given away had been taken from him. Even his fool had been executed.

Kent, who the king still did not recognize, knew Lear would never find peace in this world. He watched with relief as his friend's life gently ebbed away, his arms around his

only true daughter, Cordelia.

Albany tried to persuade Kent to take the crown, but the old earl had no use for life without Lear. "I have a journey, sir, shortly

to go," said Kent. "My master calls me. I must not say no."

So Edgar became king, and tried to rule

with honour in memory of two wronged

men: his father, the Earl of Gloucester,

and King Lear.

WILLIAM SHAKESPEARE was a popular playwright, poet and actor who lived in Elizabethan England. He married in Stratford-upon-Avon aged eighteen and had three children, although one died in childhood. Shakespeare then moved to London, where he wrote 39 plays and over 150 sonnets, many of which are still very popular today. In fact, his plays are performed more often than those of any other playwright, and he died 450 years ago! His gravestone includes a curse against interfering with his burial place, possibly to

deter people from opening it in search of unpublished manuscripts. It reads, "Blessed be the man that spares these stones, and cursed be he that moves my bones." Spooky!

MARCIA WILLIAMS' mother was a novelist and her father a playwright, so it's not surprising that Marcia ended up an author herself. Although she never trained formally as an artist, she found that motherhood, and the time she spent later as a nursery school teacher, inspired her to start writing and illustrating children's books.

Marcia's books bring to life some of the world's all-time favourite stories and some colourful historical characters. Her hilarious retellings and clever observations will have children laughing out loud and coming back for more!

More retellings from Marcia Williams

Charles Dickens'
OLIVER TWIST
Retold and Illustrated by
Marcia Williams

ISBN 978-1-4063-5692-2

Charles Dickens'
GREAT
EXPECTATIONS
Retold and Illustrated by
Marcia Williams

ISBN 978-1-4063-5693-9

Charles Dickens'
A CHRISTMAS
CAROL
Retold and Illustrated by
Marcia Williams

ISBN 978-1-4063-5694-6

Charles Dickens'
DAVID
COPPERFIELD
Retold and Illustrated by
Marcia Williams

ISBN 978-1-4063-5695-3

Available from all good booksellers

www.walker.co.uk